Frontispiece: *'Anyone fancy a fuck?' shouted Tracey as the battleship approached.*

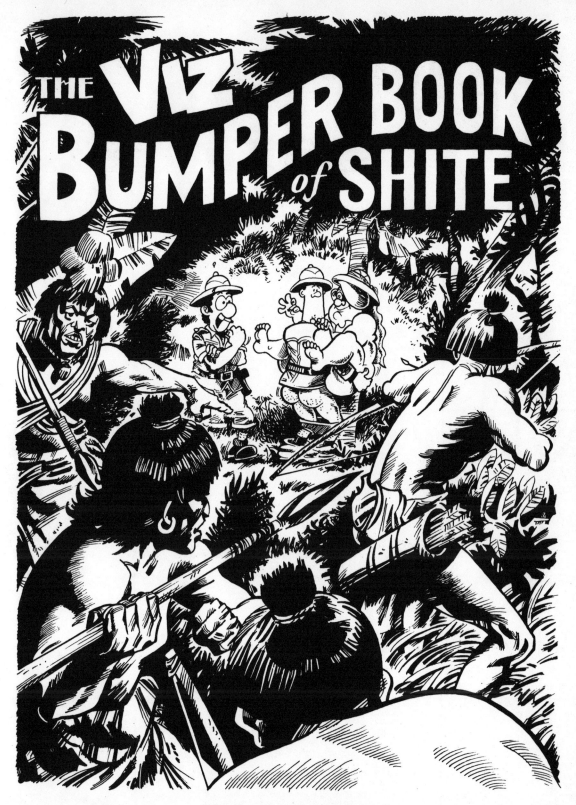

THE Viz BUMPER BOOK of SHITE

Printed in the British Empire

THE FULCHESTER UNIVERSITY PRESS

CONTENTS

PAGE

** Due to wartime restrictions on paper and ink, certain
of the above contents may not exist.*

~ INTRODUCTION ~

It has given me great pleasure editing this BUMPER BOOK of SHITE. It is a task which I relish, and I hope that you will derive as much pleasure from reading this volume as I have done from compiling it.

I pride myself in knowing what excites young boys. Healthy young boys like you. The kind of boy who has no time for girlish things, and instead would much rather play cricket with his chums. The kind of boy who would strip naked to the waist on a hot summer's day and play rough and tumble with his pals. The kind of boy who would think nothing of sharing a sleeping bag with a fellow Scout and cuddling up to preserve precious body warmth on a cold winter's night. The kind of golden-haired, blue-eyed boys for whom a day's adventure is not complete without stripping buck naked and plunging their pre-pubescent bodies into the village mill pond until the soft, downy hairs on their pert, peach-like bottoms stand erect.

Yes, proud, erect boys with a taste for British spunk. This book is for YOU! My lovely, lovely, beautiful little boys.

And girls, of course.

Yours with chumly admiration,

The Colonel.

SHORTLY...

NOW, CLASS! I'M AFRAID THAT MR. FALCONER HAS MET WITH A SLIGHT ACCIDENT AND HAS BEEN DETAINED IN HOSPITAL...

SNIGGER!

...SO YOU CAN ALL GO HOME EARLY AND DO SOME HOMEWORK!

NA-AA-AA

LET'S G' TO MY HOUSE AN' GET CHANGED INTO US ROLLERS GEAR F' THE CONCERT

THAT EVENING...

NOW LET ME DO ALL THE TALKIN' ALRIGHT!

AYE!

BAY CITY KILLERS TONITE

AYUP! DAVE!

TICKETS, PLEASE!

WE AINT GOT ANY! AW, LERRUZ IN, DAVE

AM I SUPPOSED TO KNOW YOU?

YEH! MY MATE JULIE'S BROTHER GOES OUT WI' YOUR COUSIN SALLY'S BEST MATE...

...LERRUZ IN

Why trains are LATE

Whenever we go to a railway station to catch a train, our train is always late. Sometimes trains do not arrive at all, and instead we must catch a bus or taxi to get us to our destination. Invariably we are late, for work perhaps, or for an important meeting. Let's take a look behind the scenes of Britain's busy railways and discover how exactly trains are late.

* A train's busy day begins at the train shed where mechanics inspect it, fill it with fuel and prepare it for a hard day's work. This train won't be going anywhere today. It is already late because its driver is at home in bed. He had got "backache". The passengers waiting at the station are told that their train is cancelled due to 'staff shortages'.

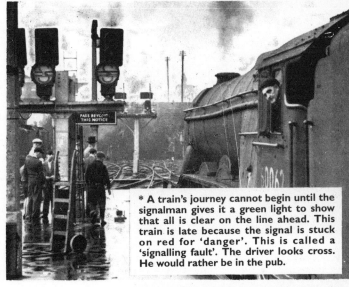

* A train's journey cannot begin until the signalman gives it a green light to show that all is clear on the line ahead. This train is late because the signal is stuck on red for 'danger'. This is called a 'signalling fault'. The driver looks cross. He would rather be in the pub.

* Signals are not the only faulty things on our railways. Here a set of points have frozen. An old man tries to mend them with an outdated piece of equipment. Despite his efforts, 'frozen points' cause many trains to be late.

Continued over...

* In winter 'snow' causes trains to be late. Nowadays trains are fitted with expensive snow blowing equipment and snow ploughs to clear the track. But these only work on certain types of snow. This train is over 4 hours late due to 'the wrong type of snow'.

In summer hot weather causes trains to be late. The heat from the sun buckles the metal tracks.

* Now it is autumn, and this diesel train hurries through the wind on the way to pick up its passengers. They wait eagerly on the platform a few miles up the line. The train is due any moment, but little do they know it won't arrive for another two hours at least. This is because leaves have fallen onto the track, and they cause its wheels to slip.

The passengers on the platform begin to get angry when their train does not arrive. Meanwhile, passengers on the following train, and on several trains behind that, are also getting angry. Their trains are all running late.

* This train is late because it is old. It is unreliable and keeps breaking down. It should have been replaced several years ago.

* This train is late because it is new. New, modern trains often have basic design faults which cause them to break down. These are known as 'minor teething troubles'.

*Here our driver is ringing up the signalman. He wonders why his train has been stopped for over an hour at a red signal. In the signal box, one hundred and fifty miles up ahead, flashing lights on his hi-technology display tell the over-worked signalman that his equipment has broken down due to lack of maintenance. He tells the driver he has no idea when his train will be able to go.

* The train crew spring into action. The driver tells the Senior Conductor that the train is stuck, and he makes an unprofessional announcement on the train's public address system. His accent is barely discernable to the majority of passengers. Consequently they do not hear his feeble apology, or the totally inadequate explanation he gives for the delay. A similar announcement is made by a disinterested sounding woman over a hopelessly inadequate public address system in the station, for the benefit of the passengers who are now scowling angrily at the train information board, and vowing never to use the train ever again. They cannot decipher her muffled, inaudible voice.

* Meanwhile back on the train the buffet should be doing a roaring trade in refreshments with their captive market of starving passengers. But the buffet is quiet, and the steward, who is normally being abrupt, (to the point of rudeness) with customers, is standing idle. This is because on a 500 mile journey from Torquay to Edinburgh, the buffet ran out of teas, coffees, hot and cold snacks, etc. at Bristol. All they have left are salted peanuts, and one slice of carrot cake with lemon icing on top.

* Back at the station another unsuspecting passenger pays a bloody fortune for a ticket. She does not know it, but her train is already 5 hours late.

15

16

CRICKET *in other*

"There isn't a more British scene, than a match of cricket 'pon village green". So wrote Wordsworth in 1744. But nowadays the popularity of our national sport has spread, and the game is enjoyed in the furthest flung corners of the globe, by chaps of every race, religion and colour. For not only has the British Empire been responsible for the spread of fairplay, correct pronounciation and good table manners across the globe, it has also taken with it that unmistakable sound of leather on willow. Yet, whilst cricket is the same game the whole world over, the rules, the object of the game and the way it is played differ greatly from nation to nation.

The frozen wastes of Iceland would be the last place you'd expect to find a game of cricket. But visit any igloo village on a Sunday afternoon and that's exactly what you'll see.

However, look closely and you may spot a few subtle differences from the English game. The Eskimo batsmen, for example, would not wield a willow bat. A large frozen fish has to suffice, for there are no trees in Iceland. As his innings proceeds the fish becomes softer, and scoring runs more difficult. Fielders must beware of holes in the ice, and marauding polar bears attracted by the smell of the bat. Running between wickets is made easier by the use of skis, however many collisions occur as cricket whites often become invisible in Iceland's blizzard weather conditions.

Cricket in the land of the rising sun is more than just a game, it's a matter of honour. Indeed, seldom does a game take place in Japan without at least two ritual suicides on the field of play. Such apparently minor matters as a dropped catch or the bowling of a wide is all that is required to prompt the highly strung oriental sportsmen to disembowel himself with the razor sharp ceremonial cricket sabre, which the umpire carries at all times. The ultimate disgrace is for the batsmen to be out without scoring. Rather than face the humiliating walk back to the bamboo pavilion he will impale himself on his own stumps.

Despite this frequent loss of life, Japan is one of the most densely populated countries in the world. As a consequence their cricket pitches rarely measure more than ten yards square.

lands

Take a trip to the Belgian Congo and you might well expect to see the Pygmy population playing some silly French game or other. But you'd be wrong. For cricket was introduced to these little fellows in 1815 by a group of M.C.C. missionaries from Trent Bridge, and it has been played there religiously ever since. Depsite an average height of only one foot five inches, the Pygmies were determined to enjoy to the full their new found game, regularly organising five-day test matches against teams from neighbouring tribes. Such was their enthusiasm for the sport that in 1894 the Pygmies clubbed together and raised the royal sum of eighteen shillings, enough to pay for the celebrated English cricketer W. G. Grace to come to the Congo for a three week intensive training visit. Unfortunately, whilst demonstrating a forward defensive prod the good doctor accidently trod on the chief of the tribe, killing the tiny fellow outright. Grace was forced to make a hasty exit, pursued by four hundred thousand spear-wielding midgets.

It is a little known fact that during the late 1930's the Government of Norway decreed that cricket was to become their national sport. Many obstacles had to be overcome, not least of which was the complete lack of any space on which to build a pitch. To solve this problem the Government spent £138,000,000 felling every last tree in Norway, and using them to build vast floating 'pontoon' cricket pitches in the fjords. However, the plan was a disasterous failure, as due to an oversight on the part of the Norwegian Minister for National Sport, the cricket season coincided exactly with Norway's winter – the six months of the year when, due to its northerly latitude, the country is plunged into total darkness. One game optimistically started in Trondheim, and Prime Minister Olaf Jurgensen ceremonially tossed the coin to decide which team should bat first. However, in the darkness the umpire was unable to find where the coin had landed, and after several hours of fruitless searching the game was abandoned. Within a week the national sport of Norway had been changed to table tennis.

JACK BLACK
& HIS DOG SILVER
IN
The Wallpaper Mystery

The summer hols were here again and young Jack Black and his dog Silver were staying with Aunt Meg in her remote crofter's cottage on the Scottish Isle of St. Claire.

WHAT CAN WE DO TODAY AUNT MEG?

I WAS THINKING OF DECORATING YOUR BEDROOM JACK. HOW ABOUT THAT?

COR! YES!! CAN I CHOOSE THE WALLPAPER?

OF COURSE YOU CAN JACK. YOU AND SILVER CAN GO ACROSS TO THE MAINLAND THIS MORNING AND CHOOSE THE PAPER FOR YOURSELVES.

COR! FANTASTIC!

WOOF!

HERE'S A TEN SHILLING NOTE FOR THE WALLPAPER, PLUS A THRUPPENNY BIT FOR YOU AND SILVER TO BUY SPANGLES WITH.

WOOF!

COR! SPANGLES! YIPPEE!

HURRY ALONG NOW OR YOU'LL MISS THE FERRY.

I HOPE WE CAN FIND SOMETHING NICE IN BLOWN VINYL, OR PERHAPS A READY PASTED FLOCK.

WOOF!

They arrived at the harbour just as the ferry was leaving.

WAIT FOR US!

ALL ABOARD!

It was a fine sunny day, and soon Jack was chatting with the old skipper Captain McFindus

TELL ME CAPTAIN. WHAT IS THAT ISLAND OVER THERE?

A dark shadow fell across the Captain's face...

OCCH! YA DINNAE WANT T'GO THERE JACK LADDIE. NO, NAE, NEVER. FOR THAT BE... MYSTERY ISLAND!

MANY FOLKS HAVE BIN' THERE BUT NONE HAVE EVER COME BACK! YOU STAY AWAY FROM THERE, Y'HEAR! STAY AWAY!!

Eventually the ferry landed.

THIS IS THE WALLPAPER STORE AUNT MEG RECOMMENDED. COME ON, LET'S GO INSIDE.

DALGLISH'S WALLPAPER WORLD

Roll up! Roll up! For WALLPAPER BARGAINS

Save £££s

50% OFF ALL ROLLS!

SUMMER SALE EVERYTHING MUST GO!!

THOUSANDS of patterns always in stock

Ye Olde Pub

SORRY SON. WE'RE CLOSED - FOR GOOD!

FOR GOOD. BUT WHY?

CLOSED

CLOSED

PUSH

I HAVEN'T SOLD A SINGLE ROLL OF WALLPAPER FOR OVER 2 YEARS. THERE WAS A TIME WHEN I COULD SELL UPWARDS OF FIFTY ROLLS A WEEK, NOT TO MENTION SCISSORS, PASTE AND OTHER ASSOCIATED ITEMS.

BUT NOW, PEOPLE DON'T SEEM TO WANT MY WALLPAPER ANY MORE!

POOR MR DALGLISH. SURELY THERE MUST BE SOME DEMAND FOR WALLCOVERINGS IN A PROSPEROUS SHRIMPING VILLAGE LIKE THIS.

Jack and Silver arrived home late that evening.

I'M AFRAID THE SHOP WAS SHUT AUNT MEG. WE COULDN'T BUY ANY PAPER.

NEVER MIND JACK. IT DOESN'T REALLY MATTER...

I'VE BEEN RINGING ALL THE LOCAL DECORATORS AND THEY'RE ALL BOOKED SOLID. NO-ONE COULD PAPER THE ROOM FOR 3 YEARS AT THE EARLIEST.

THAT'S STRANGE!

IF ALL THE DECORATORS ARE SO BUSY, WHERE ARE PEOPLE BUYING ALL THEIR WALLPAPER FROM?

The next morning Jack returned to the mainland to watch the local scampi fleet return to harbour with the night's catch.

That evening, in a picture remarkably similar to the cover of Herge's 'Black Island' Jack and his faithful companion slipped quietly away and headed for Mystery Island in a borrowed boat.

Jack landed his boat in a rocky inlet below the castle.

COME ON SILVER.

WOOF!

WOOF! GRRR! SNARL!

SILVER. WHAT HAVE YOU FOUND?

WHY... IT'S A WALLPAPER SAMPLES BOOK!

LOOK, THERE'S VYMURA, ANAGLIPTA, WOODCHIP, FLORAL, REGENCY STRIPES. WHERE DID YOU FIND THIS?

The plucky dog lead Jack to a narrow opening in the rocks.

WHY, IT'S A CAVE OF SOME DESCRIPTION.

WOOF!

A TUNNEL! WELL DONE SILVER! LET'S FIND OUT WHERE IT LEADS.

WHAT'S THAT STRANGE SOUND, COMING FROM THE END OF THE PASSAGEWAY?

AND LOOK... THERE'S A LIGHT UP AHEAD.

GOSH SILVER! I CAN HARDLY BELIEVE MY EYES.

Down below them in a vast volcanic cavern beneath the castle was a fully equipped lithographic printing press.

A PRINTING PRESS! SO THAT'S THEIR GAME. WALLPAPER COUNTERFEITING!

THE DIVER! OF COURSE. IT'S ALL BEGINNING TO MAKE SENSE.

THE EVIL FORGER HAS BEEN PRINTING BOGUS WALLPAPER THEN SELLING IT TO THE LOCAL FISHERMEN AT FACTORY DISCOUNT PRICES.

AT NIGHT HE SECRETLY SMUGGLES THE FAKE WALLPAPER INTO SHRIMP NETS WHICH THE FISHERMEN COLLECT THE NEXT DAY.

IT ALL FITS PERFECTLY. REMEMBER, WE SAW THE DIVER COLLECT HIS PAYMENT FROM THE FISHERMEN AT THE HARBOUR YESTERDAY.

25

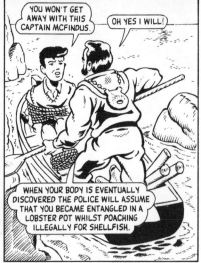

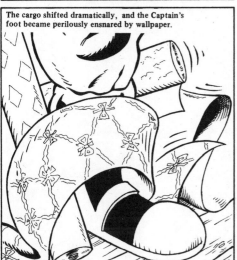

27

COME ON JACK. WE'D BEST GET OFF THIS BOAT.

THAT WALLPAPER COULD SHIFT DANGEROUSLY AGAIN AT ANY MOMENT.

WE'LL BE KEEL HAULING ALL THE LOCAL FISHERMEN THIS AFTERNOON FOR THEIR PART IN THE COUNTERFEITING PLOT. YOU CAN COME ALONG AND WATCH IF YOU LIKE.

COR! BRILLIANT! I CAN'T WAIT TO TELL AUNT MEG!

That evening over supper.

... AND THEN THEY SHOT THE CAPTAIN AND KEEL HAULED THE FISHERMEN, MANY OF WHOM WERE OLD AND FRAIL, AND DROWNED.

MY, YOU HAVE HAD AN EXCITING TIME.

AND THE GOOD NEWS IS, YOUR HOLIDAY IS BEING EXTENDED! AS THE FERRY CAPTAIN IS DEAD, THERE'LL BE NO MORE FERRIES TO THE MAINLAND 'TIL EASTER.

DOES THAT MEAN I CAN STAY FOR CHRISTMAS?

YES. MIND, THERE'LL BE PLENTY FOR YOU TO DO. THE POLICE KINDLY SOLD ME ALL THE FORGED WALLPAPER WHICH THEY CONFISCATED, FOR CASH. NOW WE HAVE ENOUGH TO DECORATE MY ENTIRE CROFTER'S COTTAGE SEVERAL TIMES OVER!

WOOF! WOOF! WOOF!

AND IT LOOKS LIKE WE'LL HAVE SOME HELP FROM SILVER TOO!

HA HA HA!

HA HA HA!

WOOF!

THE END

CD. GPD. SD. S.ECOB

FROM COW TO DOORSTEP
The Miracle of Milk

The wholesome pinta packed with vitamins and goodness begins its incredible journey in a field in the English countryside. Here cows eat grass which goes into their udders where, by miracle of nature, it is turned into milk.

The milk maid milks the cow to remove the milk, cream, butter and cheese. And yoghurt. At the dairy the milk is put in milk bottles and topped up with cream before the silver foil lids are carefully glued into place.

It's 5.30am and most of us are still asleep as the milkman makes his rounds.

It's 7.30 and time for breakfast. All over Britain millions of school children start their day with a favourite treat – milk! Who'd have thought that only three hours earlier the milk you are pouring onto your cornflakes was a clump of grass in Mother Nature's field.

ANIMALS at WAR

Ask any schoolboy who always wins the war and he'll tell you – Britain! That's because when it comes to winning wars the British are jolly well best. But it's not just our soldiers' spunk that sees off Johnny Foreigner time and time again. Over the years the British army has relied heavily on help from the animal kingdom. And its not just our four legged friend the horse who has served King and Country.

An army marches on its stomach, and during World War Two British generals considered many ways of poisoning the German food supplies. One short lived experiment was to parachute British cows, injected with deadly poison, into the fields of France.

However, the operation was a failure. Of 750 poisonous cows dropped behind enemy lines only two successfully deployed their parachutes. One suffered four broken ankles and was eaten by the French resistance, resulting in four cases of mild diarrhoea, while the other landed in a tree where it eventually starved to death.

However, all was not lost. One of the other 748 cattle which plummeted to their deaths landed on a small German motor pool in the town of Alsace, causing £45 worth of damage to a motorcycle side-car combination.

After several unsuccessful attempts by the R.A.F. to destroy the strategically vital Van de Haber railway bridge at Den Haag in Holland, the S.A.S. devised an incredible plan to sabotage the timber-built structure by introducing woodworm to its supporting piers.

Under cover of darkness, three crack S.A.S. frogmen swam 100 miles up the river Amstal before boring holes in the timbers of the bridge and releasing six specially trained woodworm larvae. Unfortunately, the daring plan was foiled when, early the following morning, a keen-eyed German guard spotted the tell-tale holes in the structure and called in Hitler's crack timber treatment division, the K.G.S. (Kuprinohl Gussellte Schtad), who successfully treated the affected timbers.

Ironically, the bridge collapsed shortly after the war due to an undetected outbreak of dry rot in the unexposed base of one of the piers.

Nowadays, squirrels are often looked upon as a pest. But in Britain's hour of need, even they had a key role to play. Professor Thomas Woodhead, a War Ministry research scientist at the top secret Bletchley Park research establishment, trained a dozen grey squirrels to relentlessly follow about and annoy several top ranking German officials. 'Woodhead's Squirrels' were a remarkable success, and became a vital weapon in the Allied arsenal. They successfully pestered and upset many top ranking Nazi targets, causing many of them to become extremely agitated and eventually lose their tempers. Their most famous victim was Hitler's deputy Rudolf Hess. After being pestered by a squirrel for nearly two years, he eventually cracked, and flew to Britain to surrender, a broken man.

Lieutenant Colonel 'Spikey' Tolhurst became better known as the 'Butterfly man of Colditz' after his dramatic escape from the notorious Nazi P.O.W. camp. Unknown to his German captors, Tolhurst, whose real legs had both been confiscated following persistent escape attempts, kept a secret stash of over 500 caterpillars in the hollow metal replacements which he had been given.

After the butterflies had hatched, Tolhurst strapped them onto his body using strands of his own hair. He then clapped his hands loudly and the startled butterflies immediately took off, hauling him to freedom over the top of the 80-foot electronic fence and past astounded Nazi guards. Once over the fence, Tolhurst caught a bus to England, where, after the war, he opened Britain's first butterfly hospital, which went bankrupt in 1947.

So many British bomber crews were lost over Germany during the war the Government ordered the R.A.F. to train monkeys to fly bombing missions. However, only one bombing mission was ever flown manned by monkeys. On a cold November morning in 1943 a Lancaster bomber, manned by six monkeys and a marmoset, took off from R.A.F. Milfield, in Northumberland, with a deadly cargo bound for Germany's industrial heartland, the Ruhr Valley.

However, four hours later the plane had to be destroyed by R.A.F. Spitfires after it had unloaded its entire cargo of bombs on the Welsh holiday town of Rhyl, killing 64 civilians. A cover-up was launched, and the incident officially blamed on a stray Nazi bomber. The monkey experiment was abandoned, and all records of it destroyed.

The Allies made several unsuccessful attempts to assassinate Hitler during the war. Perhaps the most unsuccessful of all was that codenamed 'Operation Jaws'. The plan was for a deadly man-eating Great White Shark to attack and kill the Fuhrer in front of a million of his supporters at a rally in Nuremburg. A suitable shark was captured by the Australian navy off the coast of Queensland, and transported in a large watertight box to an airfield in Scotland. The 30-foot fish was then suspended by its tail from a Spitfire at the end of a 100-foot rope, and flown to its target by a volunteer pilot. As the Fuhrer addressed the crowds the pilot made an inch-perfect swooping pass, and the vicious shark's jaws passed within snapping distance of Hitler's moustache. Unfortunately the fish had died during the 500-mile flight across the Channel, and Hitler, who appeared shocked and confused, escaped with his life.

The British were not the only ones to recruit animals during the war. Towards the end of 1944, with Monty's Eighth Army swiftly advancing across North Africa, German Field Marshall Rommel found himself desperately short of armourments. In a last gasp effort to thwart the British advance he ordered 200 elephants to be painted like tanks to fool Montgomery into over-estimating the strength of the German forces.

However, the elephants made less than convincing tanks, and after walking up and down for a couple of days they became restless and wandered off back to the jungle in search of food and water. Within weeks the Nazi hold on Africa had been broken.

Greyfriars BAGGIE

The true story of a faithful Scottish bin liner

The casual visitor to Edinburgh often passes a small statue in the Greyfriars area, unaware of the strange events that it commemorates.

After being evicted from his croft, Old Hamish set out for Edinburgh with all his possessions in a small West Highland Bag.

Living in a slum soon took its toll, but he kept the wee bag by him till the end.

All his possessions were sold for a pauper's funeral; all but the wee bag, that is. It moped about the grave until it was thrown onto a rubbish heap.

The next day the wee bag surprised everyone by blowing back to the sight of his master's grave.

Despite many efforts to shift him, "Greyfriars Baggie", as he became known, always returned to the same spot.

Baggie became a firm favourite with the local children. They used to save up rubbish especially for him.

As his popularity grew, so did Baggie. Over the years many eminent Victorians dumped the remnants of their picnics into him. Until one day

– He blew up! His epitaph was written by the Great McGonnagle:
Wind and rain come do your worst
Our faithful Greyfriars Baggie's burst.

The Adventures of FELIX CRUSOE and his AMAZING UNDERPANTS!

As originally featured in *Viz Tuppenny Illustrated Paper For Boys Own Penny Comic Illustrated, 1887. Written by Brigadier Rudyard Lewerthwaite of His Majesty's Royal Mounted Stamps, VSO, JCB, DFC and Bar. Plum. Nudge.*

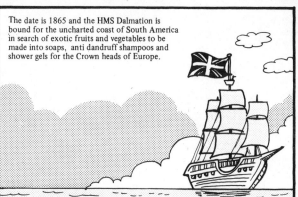

The date is 1865 and the HMS Dalmation is bound for the uncharted coast of South America in search of exotic fruits and vegetables to be made into soaps, anti dandruff shampoos and shower gels for the Crown heads of Europe.

Felix's log; Underpant date: 5th May, 1865. We have been 8 months at sea, and still no sign of land. My underpants are holding up well, but unless we reach port soon, the elastic may begin to fray...

I THINK I'LL CLIMB INTO MY HAMMOCK FOR A SHORT REST.

READER'S VOICE

BUT FELIX... YOU HAVEN'T GOT A HAMMOCK!

THAT'S WHERE YOU'RE WRONG! BY STRETCHING MY MIRACULOUS UNDERPANTS 'TWIXT TWO CABIN HOOKS MY KEX FASHION A SPLENDID HAMMOCK.

ZZZZZZ!

Within seconds the Dalmation had taken a direct hit aft of her poop deck...

34

Now with pants a'plenty Felix set about building himself a Shreddies shelter...

THIS WILL BE MY UNDERPANT HOME UNTIL I AM RESCUED.

And he put his pants to good use hunting and gathering food.

HA! GOTCHA! MY OUTSTRETCHED 'Y' FRONTS MAKE A NIFTY FISHING NET!

AND USING THESE TROLLEYS AS A SLING...

WHOOSH!

...I CAN CATCH COCONUTS!

I WILL ALSO NEED CLOTHES TO PROTECT ME FROM THE ELEMENTS...

THERE. PANT-PERFECT!

One morning while Felix was patrolling the shore...

WHAT'S THAT ON THE HORIZON? IT CAN'T BE! I DON'T BELIEVE IT!

SHIP AHOY! I'M SAVED AT LAST!

Hastily rubbing his nylon pants to create a spark, Felix ignited a huge underpant beacon to attract the ship's attention.

OH NO! THEY CAN'T HAVE SEEN ME! THEY'RE SAILING AWAY!

THERE'S ONLY ONE THING FOR IT. I'LL HAVE TO GO AFTER THE SHIP ON THIS PRECARIOUS RAFT I HAVE FASHIONED FROM DRIFTWOOD AND UNDERPANTS!

With a stiff breeze billowing in his breex and using a spare pair as a makeshift and singularly ineffecient paddle, Felix frantically headed towards the distant ship.

I'M GAINING ON HER. SHE DOESN'T SEEM TO BE MOVING.

PANTIE CELESTE

AHOY THERE! ANYONE ABOARD?

38

AMAZING BRITAIN

A few interesting facts that you probably didn't know about this wonderful country of ours

The market town of Lavenham in Suffolk is rather unusual because it's population is made up almost entirely of Dwarves. There have been Dwarves in Lavenham since the Middle Ages, which is just as well when you consider that in some of the older houses the distance between the floor and ceiling is only three feet.

Innishbogle, a small island on the west coast of Ireland, is home to that country's last remaining Leper Colony. Founded by King Brian Bogle in 673 B.C., the colony is now in the care of a group of Dublin businessmen who make sure that the residents get a pint of their favourite tipple every day.

Polperro in Cornwall solved the problem of their steep and winding streets in the most ingenious manner: they installed an escalator to carry people up from their picturesque harbour. Locals bless the day that a man in a grubby raincoat collared their vicar outside Baker Street Tube Station and offered to sell him a used London Transport Escalator.

If you look closely at the street signs in the small Welsh town of Ffestiniog you will notice that they are in Polish. After the war so many Polish slateworkers settled there that they now form the bulk of the population. Best time to visit is the feast day of St. Boris, when they all dress up in their colourful national costume and dance in the streets.

Peterhead, in the North East of Scotland, is one of the few towns that still practices ritual human sacrifice, in this case to bring good luck during the haddock fishing season. And they may have a point, because this Aberdeenshire community is now the biggest white fish port in the whole of Europe.

FROM FLOWER TO TOAST
The Magic of Honey

Honey begins its wondrous journey in the most unlikely of places – a garden. And while the gardener is hard at work, so are the flowers, 24 hours a day, making our favourite breakfast treat.

A flower is like a factory. It takes water from the soil, and sunlight from the sky, and with a little bit of Mother Nature's knowhow, makes it into honey. Now the flower's work is done, and it's time for Mr Bee to take over.

The humble bumble bee is nature's delivery van. His job is to collect honey from the flowers and deliver it safe and sound to a place where it is put in jars. On goes the lid, and the honey is then whisked away to a supermarket shelf – the next stop on it's magical journey.

The honey then makes its final voyage, via mum's grocery basket and onto your kitchen table. Yummy! Spread on hot toast, what a delicious treat! And who'd have thought that only five hours ago that delicious, sticky honey was just a twinkle in Mother Nature's eye.

Sydney Smutt's FOULMOUTH FIVE

SUMMER 1975...

BANG! BANG! BANG!

BANG! "BANG!
BANG! BANG!
BANG! BANG!

RASP! SAW! BANG!
RASP! SAW! BANG!
RASP! SAW! BANG!

EVENTUALLY...

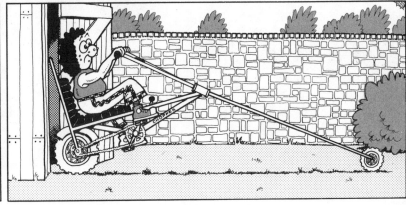

EEEH! SIDNEY, WHAT D'YU THINK Y'LOOK LIKE RIDIN' ROOND ON THIS *GHITE*?!

HOW MAN GRANDAD, THESE IS ME NEW FORKS- *MEGA EXTENTIONS!*

WHEN I WOZ A LAD WE HAD PROPER BIKES, WITH PROPER WHEELS AND PROPER FRAMES. THIS JUNK WON'T LAST FIVE MINUTES. IT'S NOT SAFE BOY.

HOW MAN GRANDAD, I'M GANNIN' TU STAY WI' ME MATES AT AUNTY PEGGY'S COTTAGE IN NORTHUMBERLAND AN' WUZ ARE AALL GANNIN' ON WU' BIKES. HOW MAN, MINE'LL BE THE EDGIEST, HEY MAN, IT'S *FANTAKKA!*

NOW LISTEN HERE YOUNG SIDNEY...

AAH NAAH! ME FORKS'VE GONE AN' BUST!

TING!

SMECK!

LATER, IN NORTHUMBERLAND...

THIS IS IT! THAT'S ME AUNTY PEGGY AN' 'ER DOG, RALPH! MEGA-BRILL!

AYE SID. TELL US AGAIN WHY IT WOULD'VE BEEN DANGEROUS TU BRING WU' BIKES.

WELL Y'SEE THESE MASSIVE LADS, TEN O' THEM, LIKE... THE' ATTACKED US FOR TU KNOCK ME BIKE 'COZ THE COULD SEE HOW GOOD IT WOZ - Y'KNAA, REALLY STRANG FORKS AN' THAT... WHY, I GOT STUCK INTU THEM, I SAVED ME BIKE AN' CHASED THEM AALL OFF LIKE, BUT I TOOK A BIRRUVA KICKIN'... BUT I CAN HANDLE THAT, ME...

...SO I THOUGHT IT WUD BE BEST FOR WU TU KEEP WU BIKES AT YEM 'COZ IF THE SAME WUZ TU HAPPEN TU ANY O' YEEZ Y'MIGHTN'T BE HARD ENOUGH TU CURP...AYE.

HMMM... SUR Y'DIDN'T JUST FAALL OFF, EH?

HAH! HAH! HAH!... WHYYYY NAAAH!... heh! heh! heh!... FAALL OFF!... NOT ME... ME!... FAAL OFF!... umph.

SIZZLE! SIZZLE!

Queen tales
FROM THE SOUTH SEAS!

The bizarre 'dental' cult of Pago Pago was first noted in the journals of the 16th Century Dutch traveller Jan Van Amstrad. "Four of us came ashore in the longboat and were immediately seized by the natives who tied us up and filled our mouths with plaster. Afterwards they took casts of our teeth and passed them around with much scowling and shaking of heads, then they all disappeared into the jungle. About an hour later they emerged smiling, cut us free, and presented each one of us with a set of dentures carved from mahogany."

Ask any British schoolboy which of our Pacific protectorates is the world's major source of phosphates and he will reply Nauru. However, the fact that large parts of the island are covered in Guano obscures it's other natural wonder; namely the Tattooed Dolphins of Nauru. Once a year in mystic collaboration with the natives, the dolphins swim to the shallows and wait patiently to be tattooed with magical symbols by the witch doctors. Due to recent contact with Europeans this tradition is dying away, and nowadays the dolphins are more likely to be covered with trademarks and graffiti.

Until recently, scientists were baffled by the strange language and culture of the Jimmi tribe from New Caledonia. The mystery was solved by a visiting Scotsman who declared that the tribesmen spoke fluent Glaswegian. Through an interpreter their chief 'Bigyin' told of how they were descended from a group of Partick Thistle supporters marooned there when the prison ship taking them to the colonies sank. Happily, New Caledonia has now been twinned with Glasgow, and to celebrate the tribesmen have just completed a replica of the Finniestone Crane, built entirely from bamboo.

The life and work of the painter Paul Gauguin is well documented and his paintings of Tahiti are known throughout our Empire. What is less well known is that this rascally Frenchman used to paint people – literally. He would sneak out at night with a bucket of creosote and cover sleeping natives with the stuff, sometimes managing to varnish a village in a night. Lacking the benefits of a British Police Force, it took several months to bring him to justice. Gauguin died soon after, still preaching the curative powers of creosote, and if the reader goes to an art gallery and sniffs one of his painting he will find that it still gives off a faint whiff of garden shed.

Black BAG

A year in the life

JANUARY

Black Bag's Busy Year starts at Hogmanay when he helps his friend P.C. Pert rescue poor creatures trapped in the snow.

FEBRUARY

February is Ramming time. Andrew brings home confused rams and keeps them in his kitchen. That's when Bag is often squeezed out of his litter basket.

MARCH

By March the lambs are stronger and more adventurous. Black Bag has a full-time job keeping them out of trouble.

APRIL

Andrew likes to think of himself as a modern shepherd. He is always trying out new methods of sheep shearing.

MAY

When tinder dry fields catch fire and farmers grab the nearest bag to beat the flames, Black Bag always makes a point of nipping off to alert the Emergency Services.

JUNE

Every year at the Peebles Show, Bag demonstrates his mastery over sheep by driving more of them up a tree than any other competitor.

# of a busy Border Binliner

Even on holiday Andrew and Bag make a perfect team. They like nothing better than to give a demonstration of their sack racing technique to crowds of delighted children.

In Peebleshire the "Glorious Twelfth" is celebrated in the time honoured fashion. Andrew flushes out the grouse with his noisy tractor while Bag drives them into the flashing blades of the binding machine.

During the breeding season impressionable ewes are often molested by badgers. But Black Bag knows how to deal with them!

At sheep dipping time Bag keeps a close eye on his master, always ready to jump in at a moments notice when the bubbles stop.

In the Peebleshire countryside November mists fall swiftly. But Andrew knows he can rely on Bag to guide him home by the safest route.

Bag loves parties. He waits patiently as the excited children gobble down their jelly and custard because he knows that it won't be long before he will be getting his share.

Biffa Bacon's Camping Capers

By Dudley Chuckles

FIRST PUBLISHED IN "Viz Comic Funnies" AUGUST 1964

52

55

INSIDE THE
TORCH

Fumble about in any young schoolboy's pocket and you're bound to put your hand on something long and hard. His torch. He uses it to find marbles under chairs, to find the outside lavatory at night, and to read his father's photographic magazines under the bedclothes. We all take the torch for granted, but what do we really know about the mysterious workings of this scientific wonder?

KEY to TORCH

(1) The Handle.
(2) The Battery.
(3) Another Battery.
(4) Torch Hook.
(5) The Bulb.
(6) Another Battery.
(7) The Front of the Torch.

HOW THE TORCH WORKS

The power for the torch is kept inside the batteries (2, 3 and 6). These are housed in the handle (1). The torch is operated using the Switch (not shown) and the power, or 'electricity', travels up the batteries (2, 3 and 6) in volts, or 'amps' and enters the bulb (5). Light then comes out the end of the torch (7).

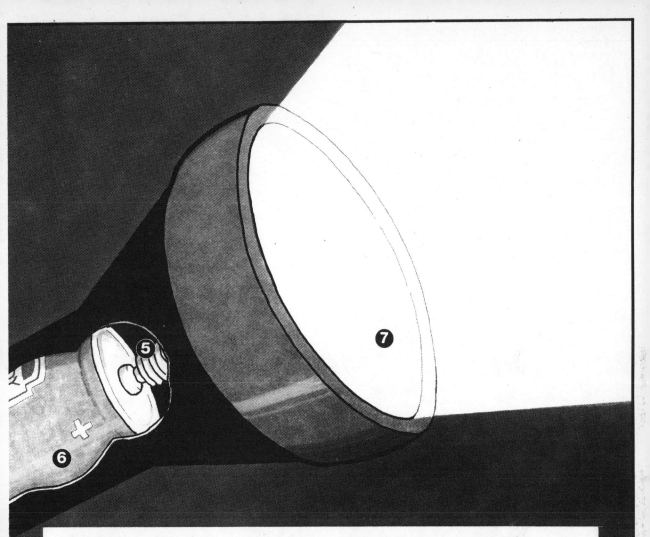

TORCHES IN ACTION

Torches are used every day by different people to do different things. Here are just two uses for the torch.

A zoo keeper using a torch to find a monkey.

A cowboy using a torch to find a Red Indian.

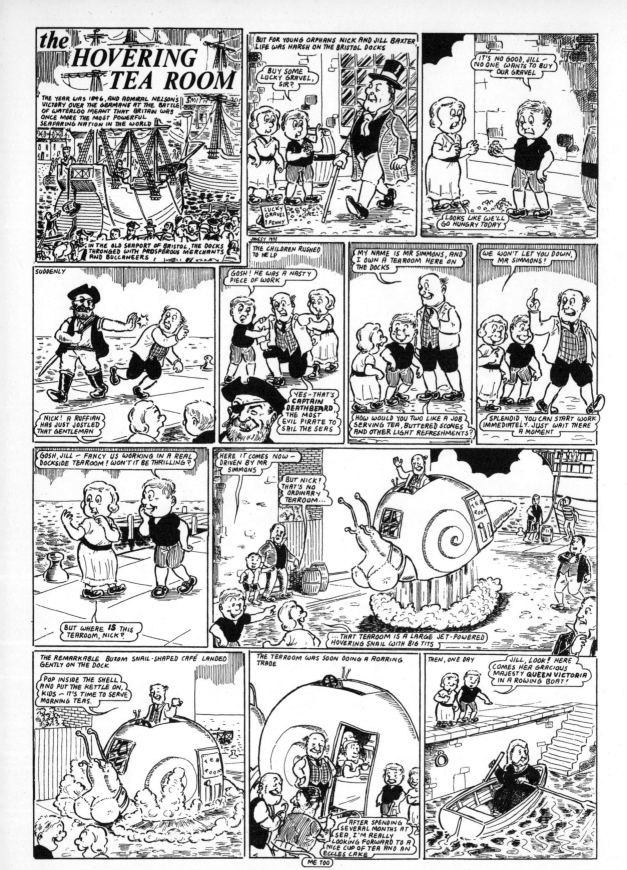

YOUR MAJESTY, WE WOULD BE HONOURED IF YOU CAME INSIDE FOR A FREE CUP OF TEA AND A MERINGUE

HOW DELIGHTFUL

SO

DID YOU HAVE AN EVENTFUL VOYAGE IN YOUR ROWING BOAT, QUEEN VICTORIA?

INDEED I DID, YOUNG MAN. I WAS ON A TOP SECRET MISSION ~ INVOLVING THE CROWN JEWELS!

DUE TO THE NUMBER OF BURGLARIES IN THIS COUNTRY, I DECIDED TO HIDE THE CROWN JEWELS AWAY FOR SAFE KEEPING

SO I ROWED OUT TO A LITTLE ISLAND IN THE PACIFIC, AND BURIED THEM IN AN OLD TREASURE CHEST ~ AND THIS IS THE MAP WHICH SHOWS IT'S LOCATION

AS THE SHORT-ARSED MONARCH PRATTLED ON, A SINISTER FIGURE AT THE NEXT TABLE WAS LISTENING THOUGHTFULLY

SHORTLY

WELL, I MUST BE GETTING BACK TO BUCKINGHAM PALACE. GOODBYE CHILDREN

GOODBYE YOUR MAJESTY

BUT OUTSIDE

NOT SO FAST, QUEEN VICTORIA ~ YOU AND YOUR TREASURE MAP ARE COMING WITH ME

UNHAND ME AT ONCE!

YOU'RE GOING TO LEAD ME AND MY PIRATE CREW TO THE ISLAND WHERE YOU BURIED THE CROWN JEWELS AH-HAR! AH-HAR!

HELP!

WE ARE NOT AMUSED!

CAPTAIN DEATHBEARD HAS KIDNAPPED QUEEN VICTORIA! WE MUST TELL MR SIMMONS

THE YOUNGSTERS FOUND MR SIMMONS MAKING ADJUSTMENTS TO THE SNAIL; BREATHLESSLY, THEY EXPLAINED WHAT HAD HAPPENED

CLOSE THE TEAROOM AND START UP THE ENGINES, KIDS

WE'RE OFF TO SAVE QUEEN VICTORIA FROM THE PIRATES!

MINUTES LATER THE BUSTY HOVERSNAIL WAS THUNDERING ACROSS THE HARBOUR IN PURSUIT OF CAPTAIN DEATHBEARD

THE PIRATES' SHIP HAD A GOOD HEAD START ~ I ONLY HOPE WE CAN FIND THEM

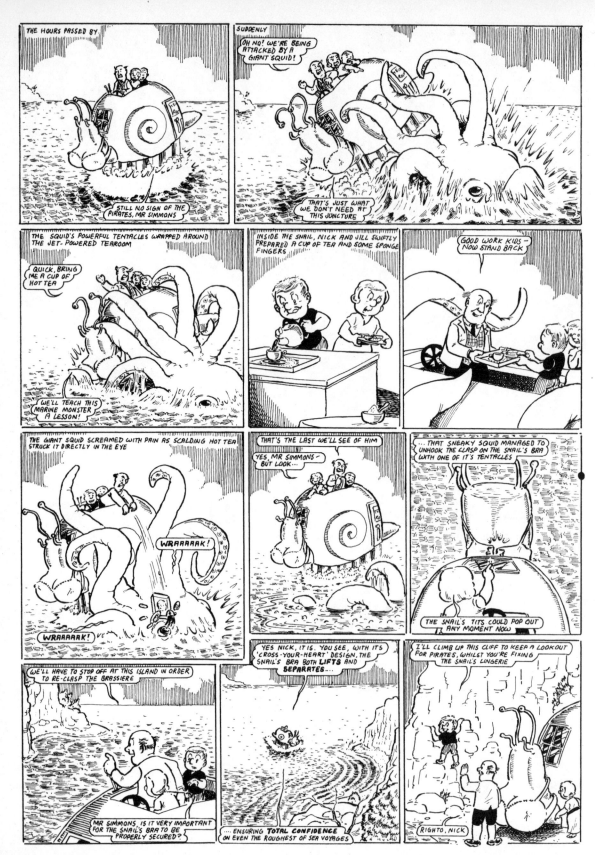

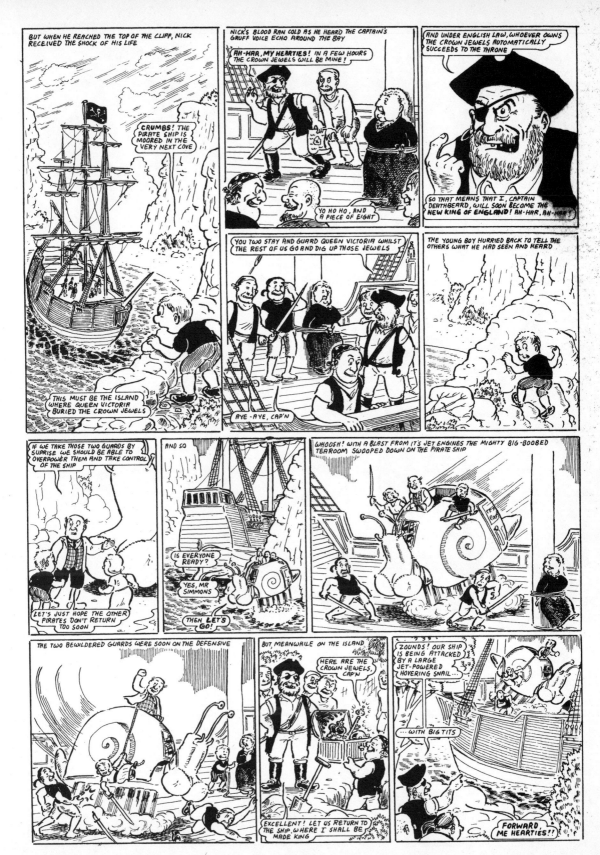

FUN & GAMES
with Roger Mellie

The fondest memories I have of my days at Fulchester Boarding School for Well Off Boys are the games my chums and I would always play together. Here's just a few. I hope you enjoy playing them as much as I did (and still do!)

Word Puzzle

Instead of English homework, why not try this literary teaser tonight. My favourite swear word is hidden in this little word grid. Can you spot it?

B	J	E	F	R	C	V	E
B	O	L	L	O	C	K	S
W	O	N	O	T	T	I	C
J	U	V	T	B	L	F	C
O	P	Q	A	A	B	V	K

Swearing with Matches

This is a spiffing way to pass the time behind the bicycle sheds inbetween puffs on a cigarette. All you need to play it are eleven matchsticks. See how I've cleverly arranged them into a rude word – 'TWAT'. See how many other swear words you can make by re-arranging the same eleven matches, then compare your results with my answers below.

The Milk Race

This is a game to play with your chums after lights out in the dorm. And you don't need a bicycle. All you need is a dirty magazine and a box of Kleenex. On the count of three everyone has to look at a dirty picture and start wanking. The first fellow to go off is the winner. And to make it more fun, the last one gets his head flushed in the lavatory. In case you don't have a dirty book, I've provided a suitable picture here. Good, isn't it?

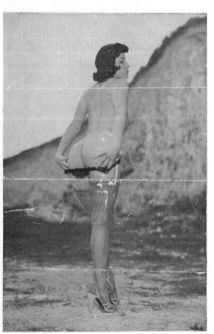

Botty Wiping

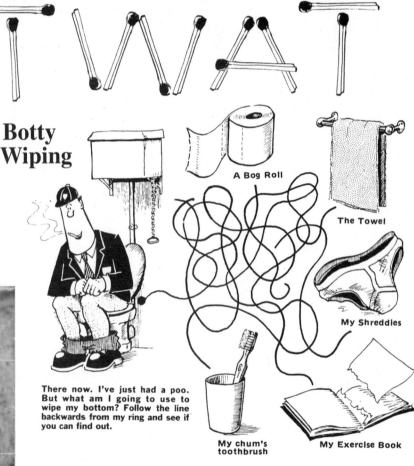

A Bog Roll

The Towel

My Shreddies

My chum's toothbrush

My Exercise Book

There now. I've just had a poo. But what am I going to use to wipe my bottom? Follow the line backwards from my ring and see if you can find out.

Graffiti Game

Look what I've drawn on the top of my desk while teacher wasn't looking! But on the second picture I've made a few changes. How many can you spot?

ANSWERS

Let's see how you did! **Swearing with Matches:** The only one I can manage is 'SHIT', with a big 'H', I hope you got a few more. **Botty Wiping:** It was my best chum's toothbrush, of course. **Graffiti Game:** I've put some spunk coming out the end. And drawn some tits next to it.

64

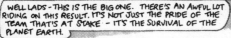

67

SHORTLY...

WELL- HERE I AM WITH THE BALL - BUT I HAVE TO ADMIT I HAVEN'T GOT A CLUE HOW I'M GOING TO BEAT THE KEEPER.

I THINK I'LL STOP AND HAVE A CIGARETTE WHILE I THINK ABOUT IT.

AEEEIIII!!!

OF COURSE! THE MATCH! IT'S AFRAID OF FIRE! YES! FIRE! THAT'S THE ANSWER!

SO...

GET BACK!

YAH! YAH!

GOAL TO FULCHESTER!

THAT MAKES IT ONE ALL !!

PHEE-EEP!

THAT'S UM HEAP FULL-TIME WHISTLE.

THAT GOAL CAME JUST IN THE NICK OF TIME, EH BOSS?

YES SYD. BUT WITH THE SCORES LEVEL AT 1-1, THE EARTH ISN'T OUT OF THE WOODS YET.

RIGHT. THE FATE OF PLANET EARTH WILL BE DECIDED BY A SUDDEN DEATH PENALTY KICK-OFF – ONE KICK EACH. FULCHESTER TO GO FIRST.

IT SEEMS RIDICULOUS THAT THE FUTURE OF THE WHOLE HUMAN RACE SHOULD BE DECIDED ON PENALTY KICKS BOSS.

YES SYD.

BUT UNDER SATURN F.A. RULES, EXTRA TIME OR A THURSDAY REPLAY ARE NOT OPTIONS. WE MUST ABIDE BY THE RULES SYD. THE REF'S DECISION IS FINAL.

BROWN FOX GETS SET TO TAKE THE FULCHESTER KICK...

SILENCE DESCENDS ON THE STADIUM...

TAKE YOUR TIME BROWN FOX.

YES. JUST RELAX.

YES. TRY TO FORGET THAT THE FATE OF THE ENTIRE PLANET EARTH DEPENDS ON THIS ONE KICK.

16,000 Fathoms to DEATH!

August 1943. Regular convoys plough across the perilous waters of the North Atlantic, providing a vital lifeline between America and the beleagured allied forces. The heavy laden vessels make easy pickings for the dreaded underwater nazi menace – the 'U' boats.

HMS Osprey is one .of several Mercury Destroyer-class frigate carriers charged with the unenviable task of escorting the convoys on their treacherous journey.

On the bridge, Captain 'Spikey' Beaumont DSO anxiously scours the horizon for the danger which may strike at any moment...

IT'S QUIET, MALTRAVERS... TOO QUIET. I DON'T LIKE IT.

CHIN UP, SKIP. TWO MORE DAYS IN THIS TUB AND WE'RE BACK IN BLIGHTY.

DAMN THIS TIN LEG!

Beaumont, veteran of over a dozen sea battles, lost his leg whilst erecting flat pack self-assembly shelving in the living room of his home in Bakewell, Derbyshire.

AHOY, CAPTAIN. MOVEMENT OFF THE PORT BOW. LOOKS LIKE WE'VE GOT COMPANY.

LET'S SEE.

IT COULD BE NOTHING, BUT I'D BETTER TAKE UP A LANCASTER FOR A CLOSER LOOK.

Beaumont fights a losing battle to keep control of the airborne giant. Spikey, veteran of many dogfights and with over 100 kills to his credit, lost his left arm below the elbow whilst putting up a larchwood lattice trellis at his mother's bungalow in Pinner.

DAMN THIS ARM!

Seconds later, Spikey Beaumont is wrestling with the controls of one of Osprey's eight Avro Lancaster reconnaissance heavy artillery bombers.

SPIKEY'S IN THE BRINEY. HE'S PRANGED HIS KITE.

BAD SHOW, SKIPPER.

BETTER LUCK NEXT TIME EH, OLD CHAP.

Meanwhile, an unseen enemy lurks nearby...

ACHTUNG! ES IST EIN SITTING DUCK. PREPARE ZE TORPEDOS - UNT BE SCHNELL ABOUT IT.

JAWOHL MEIN KAPITAN.

Captain Fritz Obergruppenfuhrer ran a tight ship aboard U-113, pride of the Luftwaffe's dreaded submarine fleet.

Back on board Osprey...

DID YOU RECCY JERRY WHILST YOU WERE UP, SPIKEY OLD BOY?

NEVER SAW A BALLY THING, GINGER. DAMN THESE GLASS EYES!

An Olympic gold medal winning marksman, Spikey Beaumont had tragically lost both his eyes whilst pinning up bunting at his Auntie Jean's local church fete in Wimbourne

I SAY - IT'S VERA LYNNS BIRTHDAY. ANYONE FOR BUBBLY?

OH I SAY. GOOD SHOW.

TOP HOLE.

The fearless skiper packed his mouth and hat with dynamite before loading himself into the salvaged torpedo tube.

BREAK A LEG, SKIP.

5...4...3...2...1...

...FIRE!

NOW TO TEACH THAT SQUAREHEAD A LESSON HE WON'T FORGET IN A HURRY.

TALLY HO! SPIKEY'S BANG ON COURSE!

AAARGH!

The stricken U-boat sank in seconds.

HOORAH!

Moments later...

WELL DONE, SKIPPER. BULLSEYE!

THANKS CHAPS. BUT BOY, HAVE I GOT A SORE HEAD!

Between October 1943 and August 1947, 436 German submarines were destroyed by the English navy in the North Atlantic. Thanks to the bravery of men like 'Spikey' Beaumont, vital convoys were able to reach their destinations, and allied forces gained control of the seas. Britannia once again ruled the waves, Hitler was routed in Europe and peace returned to the World. Beaumont finished the war as a rear Admiral in the RAF, and was killed in 1949 whilst repairing a bird table in the garden of his cousin Nora's house just outside Barrow-in-Furness. He was posthumously awarded the Victoria Cross by a grateful nation.

THE END

SPOILT BASTARD'S BIG TOP ADVENTURE

FEATURING PRINCESS TIFFANY

SPLAT!

PUNT!

HOORAY FOR OVALTINI

MUMMY, MUMMY. LOOK AT THE LITTLE FAT ONE WITH FISH DOWN HIS TROUSERS. DOESN'T HE LOOK STUPID.

YES!

LATER...

BOO HOO! SOB!

TIMMY! WHAT'S WRONG?

OH, I'M FED UP. I'M A LAUGHING STOCK

I WANT TO BE A STAR LIKE YOU, PRINCESS TIFFANY. WHEN YOU'RE UP ON THE TRAPEZE, PEOPLE LOVE YOU. THEY JUST LAUGH AT ME. IT'S NOT FAIR!

OH, TIMMY...

...YOU'LL ALWAYS BE MY STAR, YOU KNOW THAT

THERE, THERE TIMMY, MY LOVE

BOO HOO

WEEKS LATER AGAIN...

TIMMY...

EH!?

OVALTINI

...YOU CAN GET CHANGED. I'M AFRAID TONIGHT'S SHOW IS CANCELLED. THE GREAT STROMBOLLI, PRINCESS TIFFANY'S PARTNER HAS STRAINED HIS FINGER.

WAIT A MINUTE. I'LL TAKE HIS PLACE

YOU? YOU'RE JUST A CLOWN

NO! I CAN DO IT. I KNOW I CAN

OH PLEASE, PLEASE, PLEASE LET ME GO UP THERE WITH HER...

77

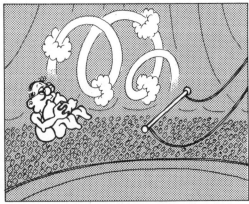

THE Viz BUMPER BOOK of SHITE

for OLDER BOYS & GIRLS

Written on location at Millom, Cumbria at the generous invitation of
Brigadier Lewerthwaite, and at the House of Viz, Newcastle upon Tyne, by
Chris Donald, Graham Dury, Simon Thorp and Simon Donald.

With additional contributions by Davey Jones and Graham Murdoch.
Additional illustration by Simon Ecob and Mr Lewis Stringer.

ISBN 1 870870 131

Published in the British Empire by John Brown Publishing Limited,
The Boathouse, Crabtree Lane, Fulham, London SW6 6LU.

First printing August 1993.

Printed and bound in Great Britain. Long live the King.

Backispiece: **'With a single shot Caruthers bagged his tenth elephant of the day'.**